Success
Assessment Papers

Non-Verbal
Reasoning

age 9 – 10

Pamela Macey

paper number for quick reference

integrated mark scheme

example at the beginning of each section of questions

clear instructional text

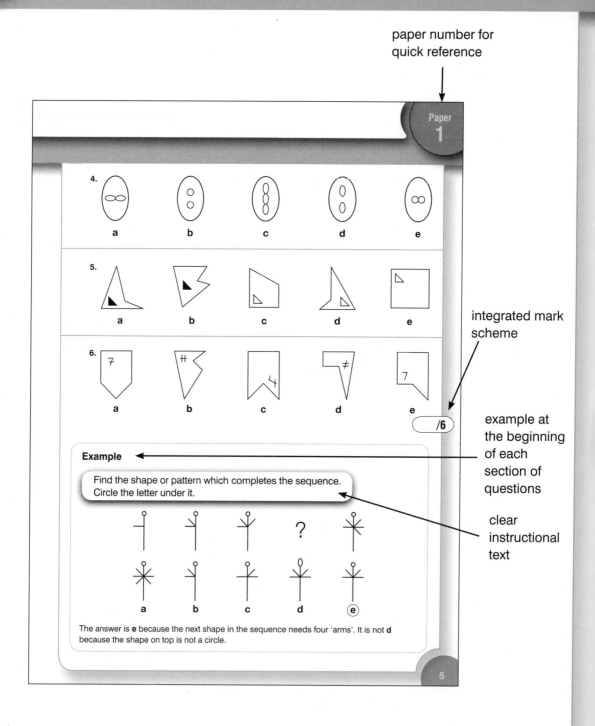

Paper 1

4.

a b c d e

5.

a b c d e

6.

a b c d e

/6

Example

Find the shape or pattern which completes the sequence. Circle the letter under it.

?

a b c d e

The answer is **e** because the next shape in the sequence needs four 'arms'. It is not **d** because the shape on top is not a circle.

5

Contents

PAPER 1

Example

Which is the odd one out? Circle the letter under it.

a   b   (c)   d   e

The answer is **c** because it is the only one that has + instead of ×. In this example, the position of the shapes is not relevant.

Now try these. Which is the odd one out? Circle the letter under it.

1.

a   b   c   d   e

2.

a   b   c   d   e

3.

a   b   c   d   e

4.

   a   b   c   d   e

5.

   a   b   c   d   e

6.

   a   b   c   d   e

/6

Example

Find the shape or pattern which completes the sequence.
Circle the letter under it.

        ?

   a   b   c   d   (e)

The answer is **e** because the next shape in the sequence needs four 'arms'. It is not **d** because the shape on top is not a circle.

Now try these. Find the shape or pattern which completes the sequence. Circle the letter under it.

7.

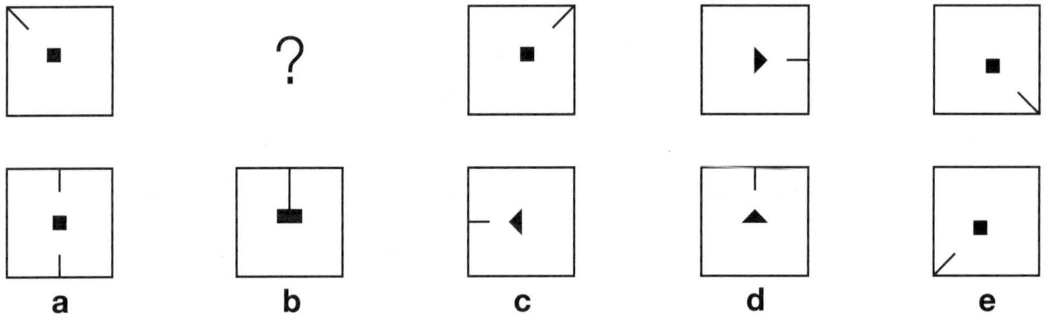

a   b   c   d   e

8.

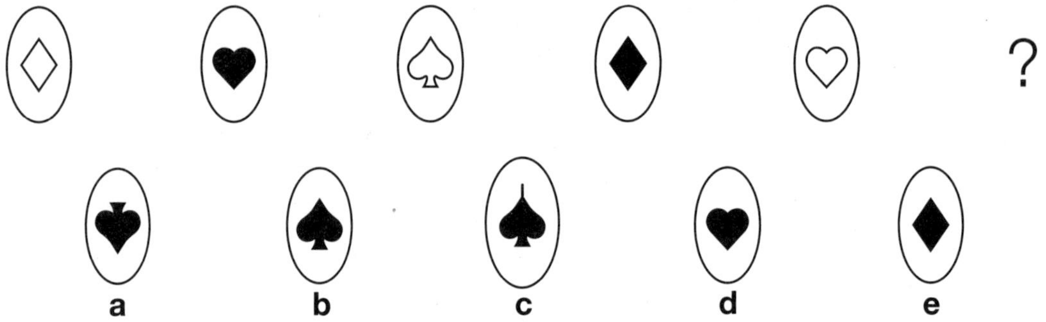

a   b   c   d   e

9.

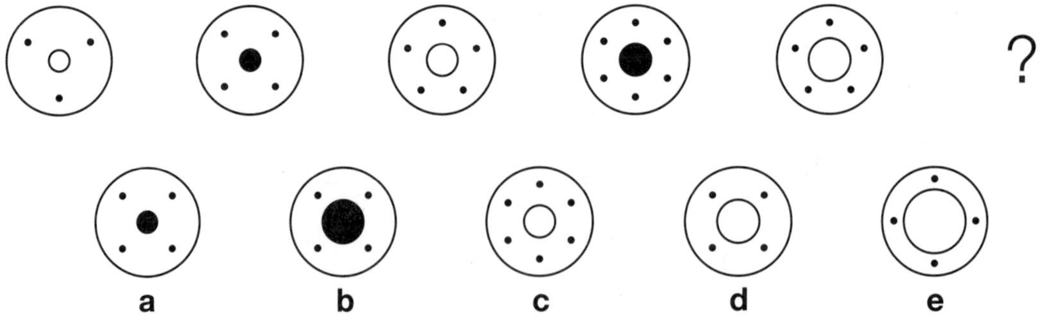

a   b   c   d   e

10.

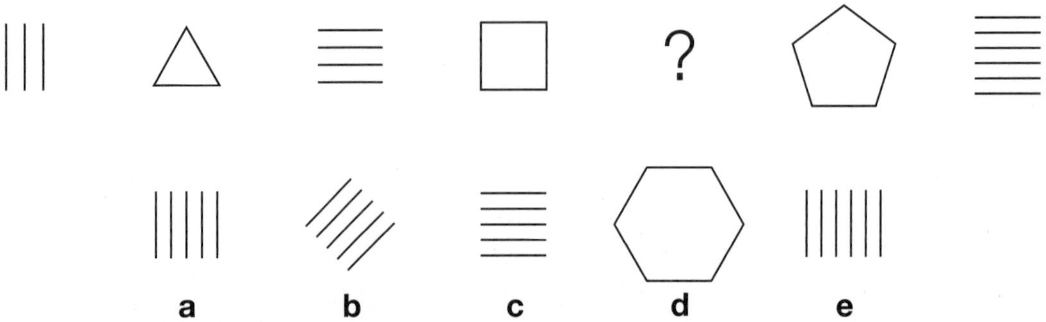

a   b   c   d   e

11.

?

a   b   c   d   e

/5

Example

Match the missing part of the second pair in a similar way to the first pair. Circle the letter under the missing part.

 as

⇒

a   b   c   d   e

The answer is **d**.

Now try these. Match the missing part of the second pair in a similar way to the first pair. Circle the letter under the missing part.

12.

 ⇒   as

a   b   c   d   e

13.

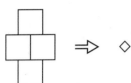 

a   b   c   d   e

14.

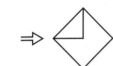

a   b   c   d   e

15.

a   b   c   d   e

16. 969 ⇒ **6** as

a   b   c   d   e

/5

Example

Look at the shapes and patterns. Work out the code for each question by putting the pattern and shape together. Circle the letter under the code.

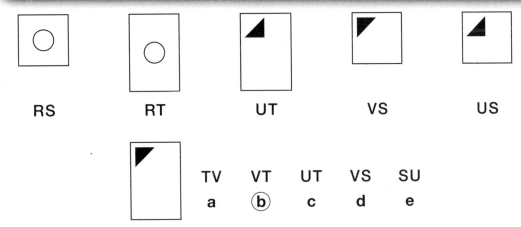

RS   RT   UT   VS   US

TV   VT   UT   VS   SU
a   (b)   c   d   e

To find the answer, you need to work out what each letter stands for. Notice that the first letter stands for the shape inside – in this case, **V**. The second letter stands for the outer shape. In this case, **T** stands for the rectangle, so the answer is **VT** and the letter **b** should be circled.

Now try these. Look at these shapes and patterns. Work out the code for the questions below by putting the pattern and shape together. Circle the letter under the code.

17.

FO   SO   FN   FM   SM

    SN   SO   FN   FM   NS
a   b   c   d   e

18.

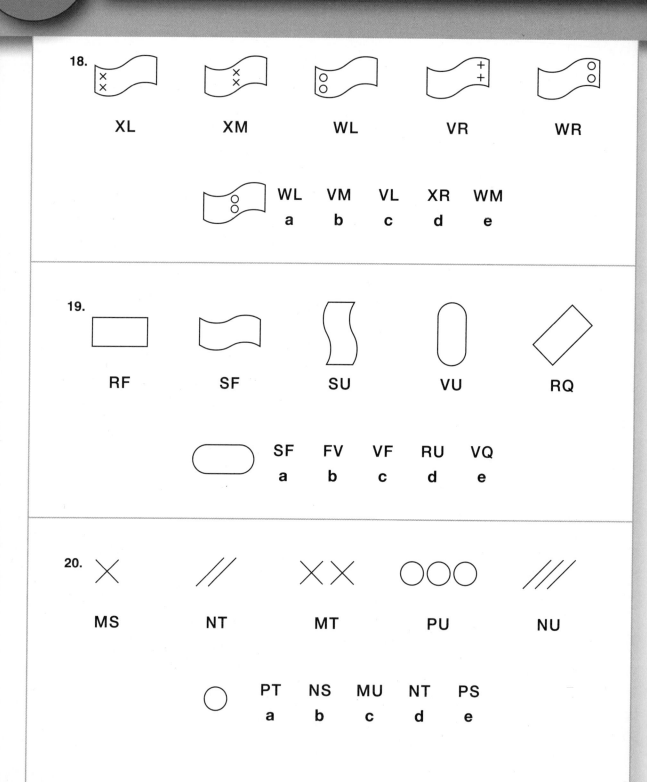

| XL | XM | WL | VR | WR |

| WL | VM | VL | XR | WM |
| a | b | c | d | e |

19.

| RF | SF | SU | VU | RQ |

| SF | FV | VF | RU | VQ |
| a | b | c | d | e |

20.

| MS | NT | MT | PU | NU |

| PT | NS | MU | NT | PS |
| a | b | c | d | e |

21.

SU   SW   TW   RV   RU

          SV   SU   RW   TV   TU

          a   b   c   d   e

/5

Example

Complete the grid by finding the missing square.
Circle the letter under the square.

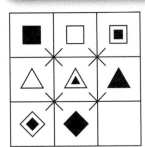

          a   b   c   d   e

The answer is **d** because the white diamond completes the row of diamonds in the grid in a similar way to the first two rows. Also, the diagonal line in the corner of **d** makes the whole grid symmetrical.

Now try these. Complete the grid by finding the missing square.
Circle the letter under the square.

22.
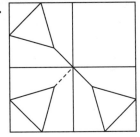

          a   b   c   d   e

23.

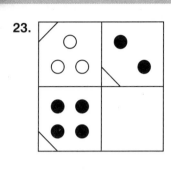 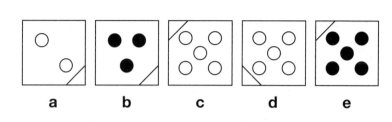

a   b   c   d   e

24.

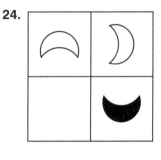 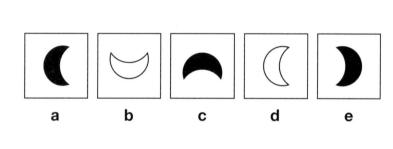

a   b   c   d   e

25.

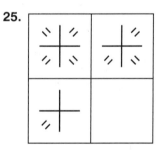 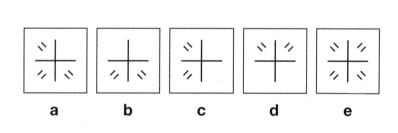

a   b   c   d   e

26.

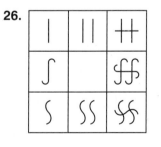 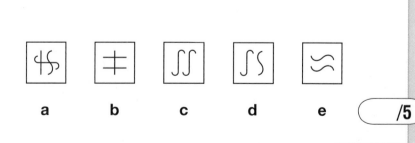

a   b   c   d   e

/5

/26

PAPER 2

Example

Match the missing part of the second pair in a similar way to the first pair. Circle the letter under the missing part.

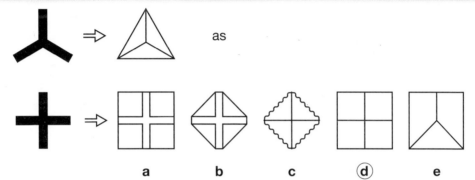

as

a   b   c   (d)   e

The answer is **d.**

Now try these. Match the missing part of the second pair in a similar way to the first pair. Circle the letter under the missing part.

1.

as

a   b   c   d   e

2.

as

a   b   c   d   e

3. ⇒ as

 ⇒

         a   b   c   d   e

4. □ ⇒ ○ as

 ⇒

         a   b   c   d   e

5. □ ⇒ ▱ as

 ⇒

         a   b   c   d   e

6. □ ⇒ □□□ as

 ⇒

         a   b   c   d   e

/6

Example

Complete the grid by finding the missing square.
Circle the letter under the square.

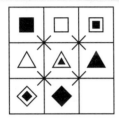

a   b   c   (d)   e

The answer is **d** because the white diamond completes the row of diamonds in the grid in a similar way to the first two rows. Also, the diagonal line in the corner of **d** makes the whole grid symmetrical.

Now try these. Complete the grid by finding the missing square.
Circle the letter under the square.

7.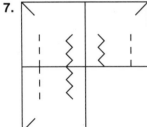

a   b   c   d   e

8.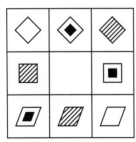

a   b   c   d   e

9.

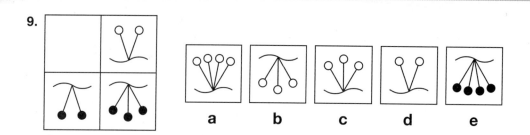

a   b   c   d   e

10.

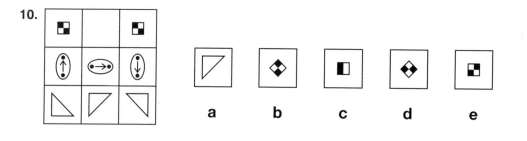

a   b   c   d   e

11.

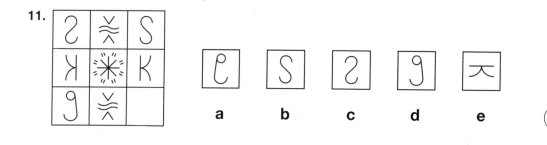

a   b   c   d   e

/5

Example

> Which is the odd one out? Circle the letter under it.

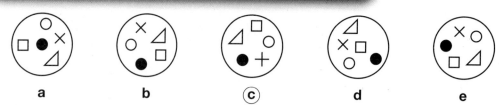

a   b   c   d   e

The answer is **c** because it is the only one that has + instead of ×. In this example, the position of the shapes is not relevant.

Now try these. Which is the odd one out? Circle the letter under it.

12.

a   b   c   d   e

13.

a   b   c   d   e

14.

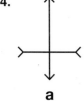 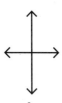 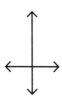 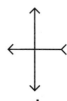 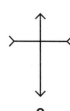

a   b   c   d   e

15.

a   b   c   d   e

16.

a   b   c   d   e

/5

Example

Find the shape or pattern which completes the sequence.
Circle the letter under it.

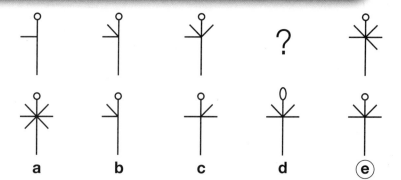

The answer is **e** because the next shape in the sequence needs four 'arms'. It is not **d** because the shape on top is not a circle.

Now try these. Find the shape or pattern which completes
the sequence. Circle the letter under it.

17.

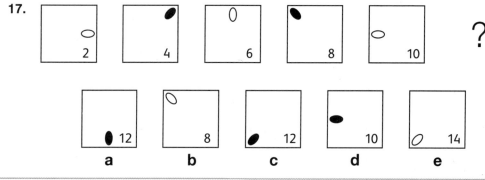

18.

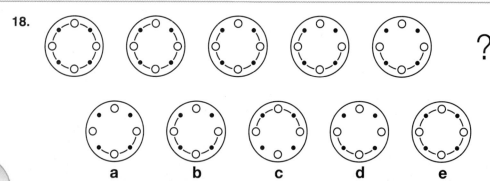

19.

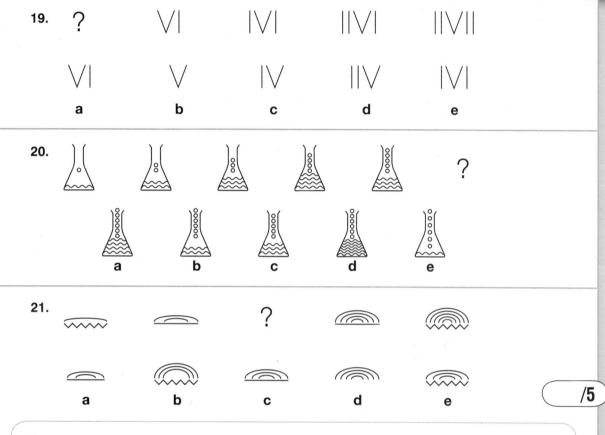

20.

21.

/5

Example

Look at the shapes and patterns. Work out the code for each question by putting the pattern and shape together. Circle the letter under the code.

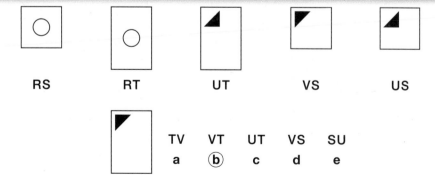

To find the answer, you need to work out what each letter stands for. Notice that the first letter stands for the shape inside – in this case, **V**. The second letter stands for the outer shape. In this case, **T** stands for the rectangle, so the answer is **VT** and the letter **b** should be circled.

Now try these. Look at these shapes and patterns. Work out the code for the questions below by putting the pattern and shape together. Circle the letter under the code.

22.

| TS | QW | ZW | PS | TW |

| | ZW | ZS | PW | TS | QS |
| | a | b | c | d | e |

23.

| FK | GK | FJ | HL | IL |

| | GJ | GL | HL | FL | IK |
| | a | b | c | d | e |

24.

| XR | WR | WS | XS | XT |

| | WT | WS | XT | XS | WR |
| | a | b | c | d | e |

25.

| FJ | GK | GL | HJ | IK |

| | FL | HK | FK | IJ | GK |
| | a | b | c | d | e |

26.

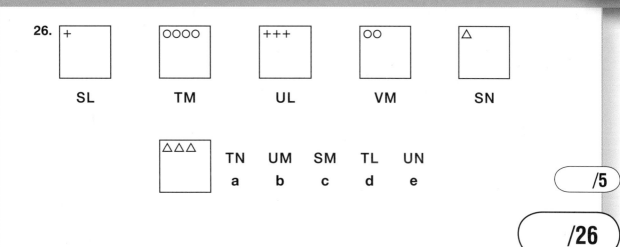

SL TM UL VM SN

TN UM SM TL UN
a b c d e

/5

/26

Example

Complete the grid by finding the missing square.
Circle the letter under the square.

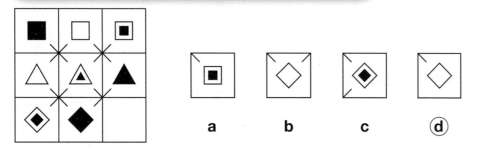

a b c d e

The answer is **d** because the white diamond completes the row of diamonds in the grid in a similar way to the first two rows. Also, the diagonal line in the corner of **d** makes the whole grid symmetrical.

Now try these. Complete the grid by finding the missing square.
Circle the letter under the square.

1.

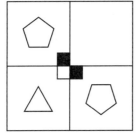

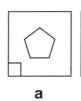

    a   b   c   d   e

2.

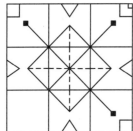

    a   b   c   d   e

3.

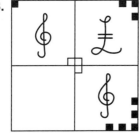

    a   b   c   d   e

4.

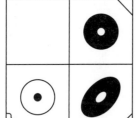

    a   b   c   d   e

5.

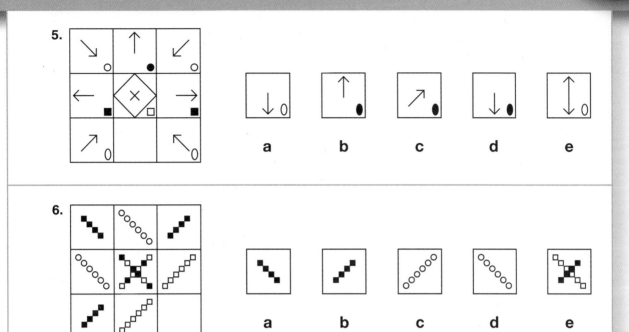

a   b   c   d   e

6.

a   b   c   d   e

Example

Look at the shapes and patterns. Work out the code for each question by putting the pattern and shape together. Circle the letter under the code.

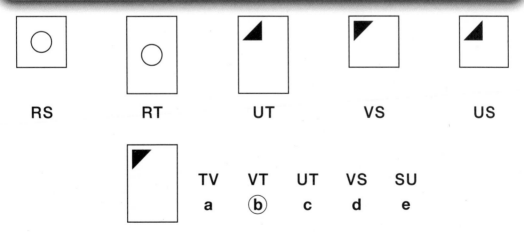

RS   RT   UT   VS   US

TV   VT   UT   VS   SU

a   b   c   d   e

To find the answer, you need to work out what each letter stands for. Notice that the first letter stands for the shape inside – in this case, **V**. The second letter stands for the outer shape. In this case, **T** stands for the rectangle, so the answer is **VT** and the letter **b** should be circled.

Now try these. Look at these shapes and patterns. Work out the code for the questions below by putting the pattern and shape together. Circle the letter under the code.

7.

LI   MH   NI   OH   PI

OH	OI	NH	MI	IO
a	b	c	d	e

8.

MQ   NR   MS   OQ   PT

PS	MQ	PR	MR	OR
a	b	c	d	e

9.

TM   TN   SM   SO   SP

TP	PT	TO	SN	SP
a	b	c	d	e

10.

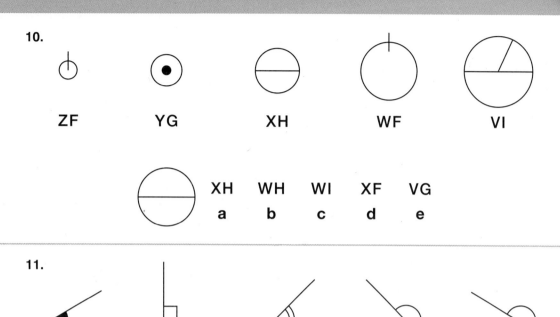

ZF　　　YG　　　XH　　　WF　　　VI

	XH	WH	WI	XF	VG
	a	b	c	d	e

11.

FM　　　GN　　　HO　　　IP　　　JP

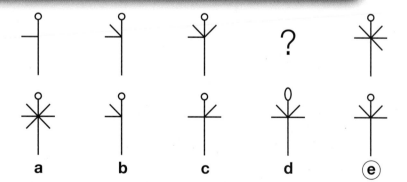

	IM	HP	FN	IO	JO
	a	b	c	d	e

/5

Example

Find the shape or pattern which completes the sequence.
Circle the letter under it.

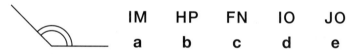

a　　　b　　　c　　　d　　　e

The answer is **e** because the next shape in the sequence needs four 'arms'. It is not **d** because the shape on top is not a circle.

Now try these. Find the shape or pattern which completes the sequence. Circle the letter under it.

12.

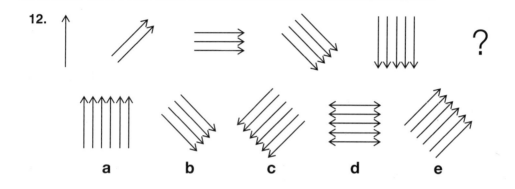

13.

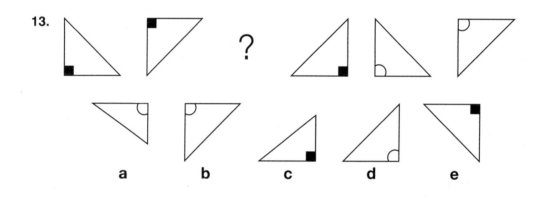

14.

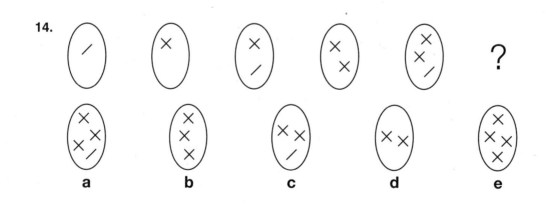

15.

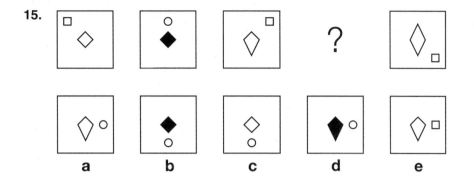

| a | b | c | d | e |

16.

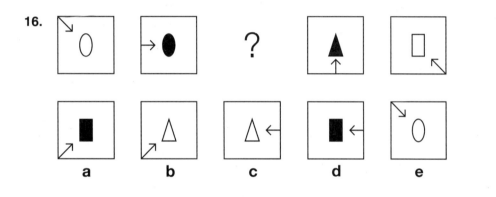

| a | b | c | d | e |

/5

Example

Which is the odd one out? Circle the letter under it.

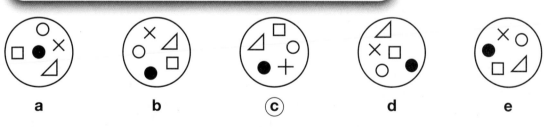

| a | b | c | d | e |

The answer is **c** because it is the only one that has + instead of ×. In this example, the position of the shapes is not relevant.

Now try these. Which is the odd one out? Circle the letter under it.

17.

a

b

c

d

e

18.

a

b

c

d

e

19.

a

b

c

d

e

20.

a

b

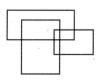

c

d

e

21.

a

b

c

d

e

/5

Example

Match the missing part of the second pair in a similar way to the first pair. Circle the letter under the missing part.

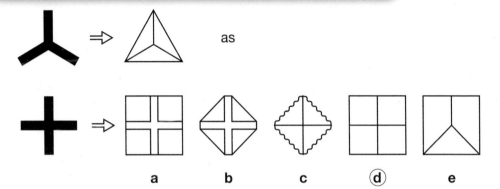

a	b	c	d	e

The answer is **d.**

Now try these. Match the missing part of the second pair in a similar way to the first pair. Circle the letter under the missing part.

22.

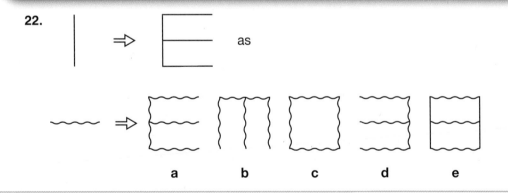

a	b	c	d	e

23.

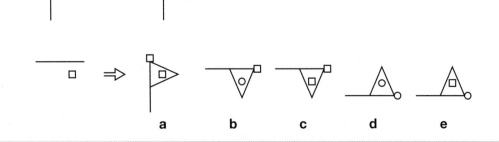

a	b	c	d	e

24.

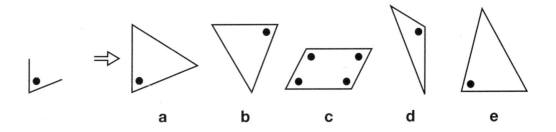

           a   b   c   d   e

25. 4 ⇒ 5   as

2 ⇒ 25   8   24   3   1

         a   b   c   d   e

26.

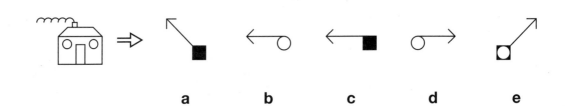

         a   b   c   d   e

/5

/26

PAPER 4

Example

Find the shape or pattern which completes the sequence. Circle the letter under it.

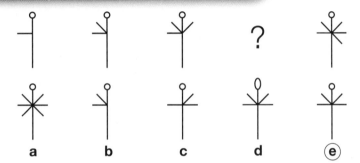

a   b   c   d   e

The answer is **e** because the next shape in the sequence needs four 'arms'. It is not **d** because the shape on top is not a circle.

Now try these. Find the shape or pattern which completes the sequence. Circle the letter under it.

1.

a   b   c   d   e

2.

a   b   c   d   e

3.

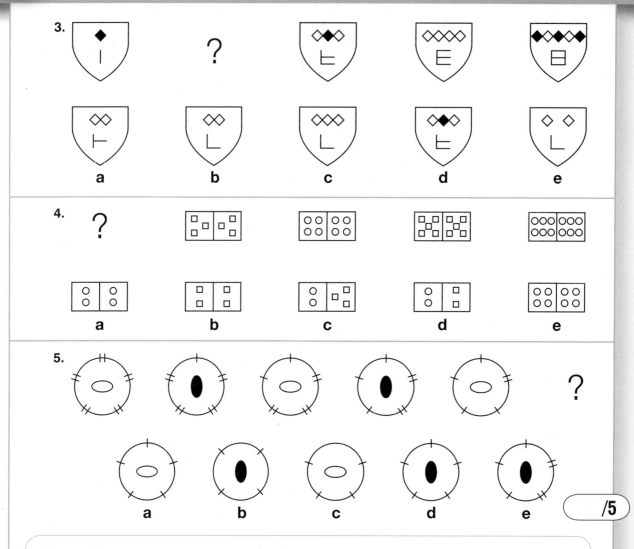

4.

5.

/5

Example

Which is the odd one out? Circle the letter under it.

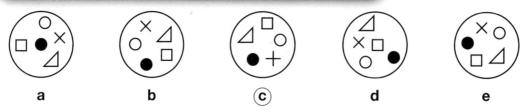

a b c d e

The answer is **c** because it is the only one that has + instead of ×. In this example, the position of the shapes is not relevant.

Now try these. Which is the odd one out? Circle the letter under it.

6.

a   b   c   d   e

7.

a   b   c   d   e

8.

a   b   c   d   e

9.

a   b   c   d   e

10.

a   b   c   d   e

/5

Example

Look at the shapes and patterns. Work out the code for each question by putting the pattern and shape together. Circle the letter under the code.

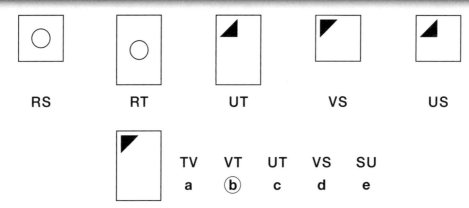

RS	RT	UT	VS	US

TV   VT   UT   VS   SU

a   ⓑ   c   d   e

To find the answer, you need to work out what each letter stands for. Notice that the first letter stands for the shape inside – in this case, **V**. The second letter stands for the outer shape. In this case, **T** stands for the rectangle, so the answer is **VT** and the letter **b** should be circled.

Now try these. Look at these shapes and patterns. Work out the code for the questions below by putting the pattern and shape together. Circle the letter under the code.

11.

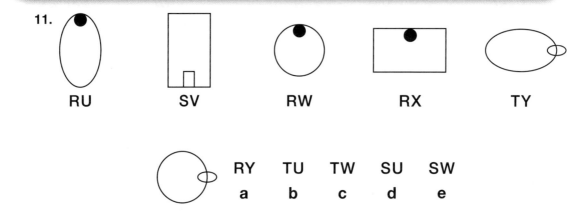

RU	SV	RW	RX	TY

RY   TU   TW   SU   SW

a   b   c   d   e

Success

Assessment Papers

Non-Verbal Reasoning

age 9 – 10

Answer booklet

Answer booklet: Non-Verbal Reasoning age 9–10

Paper 1	Paper 2	Paper 3
1. d	1. e	1. d
2. e	2. d	2. c
3. a	3. a	3. e
4. c	4. b	4. b
5. b	5. d	5. d
6. e	6. e	6. a
7. d	7. a	7. b
8. b	8. e	8. c
9. b	9. c	9. a
10. a	10. e	10. b
11. d	11. a	11. d
12. b	12. d	12. c
13. c	13. a	13. e
14. e	14. d	14. b
15. a	15. c	15. d
16. b	16. b	16. b
17. a	17. c	17. c
18. e	18. d	18. b
19. c	19. b	19. c
20. e	20. b	20. b
21. d	21. e	21. a
22. e	22. b	22. b
23. c	23. b	23. c
24. a	24. a	24. a
25. b	25. c	25. d
26. c	26. e	26. b

Paper 4

1. c
2. e
3. b
4. a
5. d
6. c
7. e
8. e
9. c
10. a
11. c
12. d
13. e
14. b
15. d
16. c
17. a
18. e
19. b
20. c
21. c
22. c
23. b
24. c
25. d
26. e

Paper 5

1. b
2. a
3. a
4. c
5. c
6. e
7. b
8. d
9. a
10. b
11. e
12. a
13. e
14. c
15. d
16. e
17. a
18. c
19. c
20. a
21. a
22. c
23. a
24. c
25. a
26. d

Paper 6

1. e
2. a
3. d
4. e
5. c
6. d
7. e
8. a
9. e
10. a
11. d
12. b
13. c
14. c
15. e
16. c
17. a
18. d
19. b
20. b
21. d
22. a
23. c
24. e
25. d
26. c

Paper 7

1. b
2. d
3. c
4. a
5. b
6. e
7. c
8. b

9. e	**15.** b	**21.** a
10. d	**16.** c	**22.** d
11. a	**17.** d	**23.** a
12. c	**18.** e	**24.** e
13. d	**19.** b	**25.** b
14. e	**20.** b	**26.** c

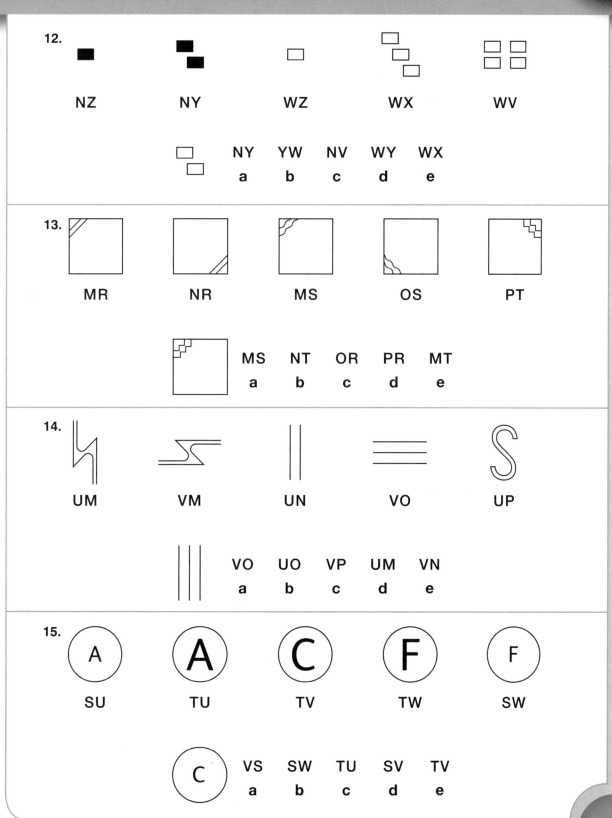

12.

| NZ | NY | WZ | WX | WV |

| | NY | YW | NV | WY | WX |
| | a | b | c | d | e |

13.

| MR | NR | MS | OS | PT |

| | MS | NT | OR | PR | MT |
| | a | b | c | d | e |

14.

| UM | VM | UN | VO | UP |

| | VO | UO | VP | UM | VN |
| | a | b | c | d | e |

15.

| A | A | C | F | F |
| SU | TU | TV | TW | SW |

| C | VS | SW | TU | SV | TV |
| | a | b | c | d | e |

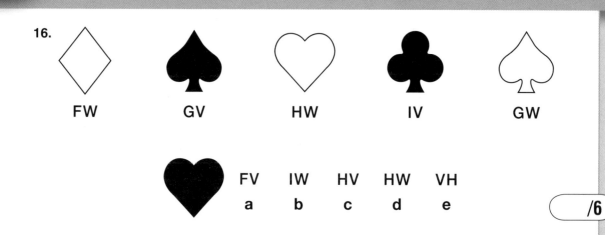

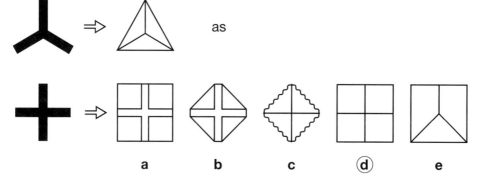

16.

FW   GV   HW   IV   GW

FV   IW   HV   HW   VH
a   b   c   d   e

/6

Example

Match the missing part of the second pair in a similar way to the first pair. Circle the letter under the missing part.

⇒   as

⇒

a   b   c   (d)   e

The answer is **d.**

Now try these. Match the missing part of the second pair in a similar way to the first pair. Circle the letter under the missing part.

17.

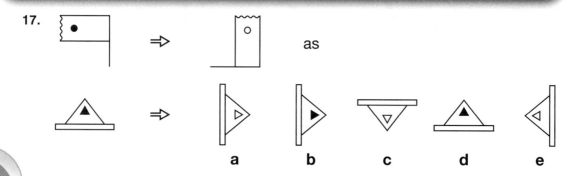

⇒   as

⇒

a   b   c   d   e

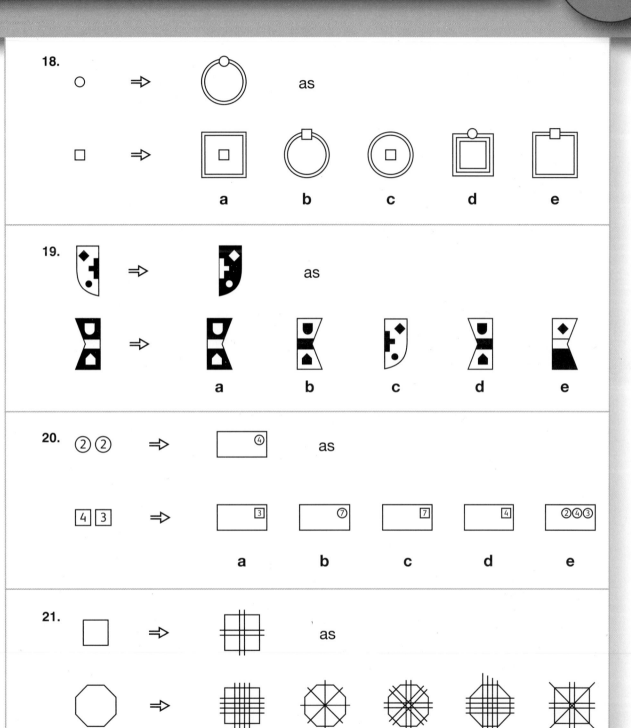

18.

a b c d e

19.

a b c d e

20.

a b c d e

21.

a b c d e

Example

Complete the grid by finding the missing square.
Circle the letter under the square.

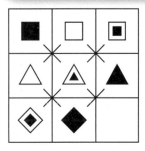

a   b   c   (d)   e

The answer is **d** because the white diamond completes the row of diamonds in the grid in a similar way to the first two rows. Also, the diagonal line in the corner of **d** makes the whole grid symmetrical.

Now try these. Complete the grid by finding the missing square.
Circle the letter under the square.

22.

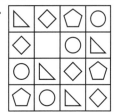

a   b   c   d   e

23.

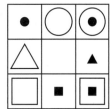

a   b   c   d   e

24.

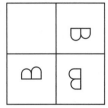

a   b   c   d   e

25.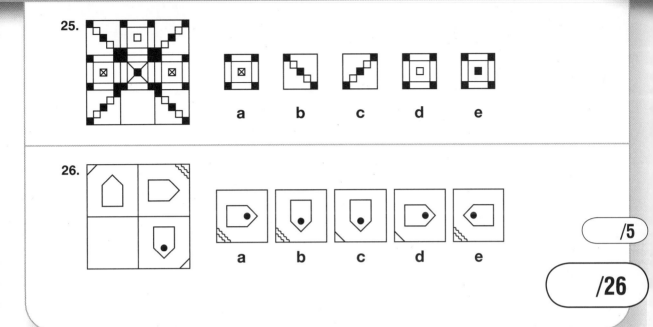

    a   b   c   d   e

26.

    a   b   c   d   e

/5

/26

PAPER 5

Example

> Look at the shapes and patterns. Work out the code for each question by putting the pattern and shape together. Circle the letter under the code.

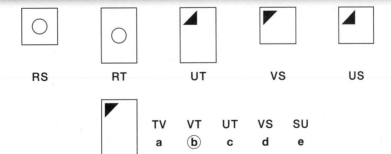

RS   RT   UT   VS   US

TV VT UT VS SU
a   (b) c   d   e

To find the answer, you need to work out what each letter stands for. Notice that the first letter stands for the shape inside – in this case, **V**. The second letter stands for the outer shape. In this case, **T** stands for the rectangle, so the answer is **VT** and the letter **b** should be circled.

Now try these. Look at these shapes and patterns. Work out the code for the questions below by putting the pattern and shape together. Circle the letter under the code.

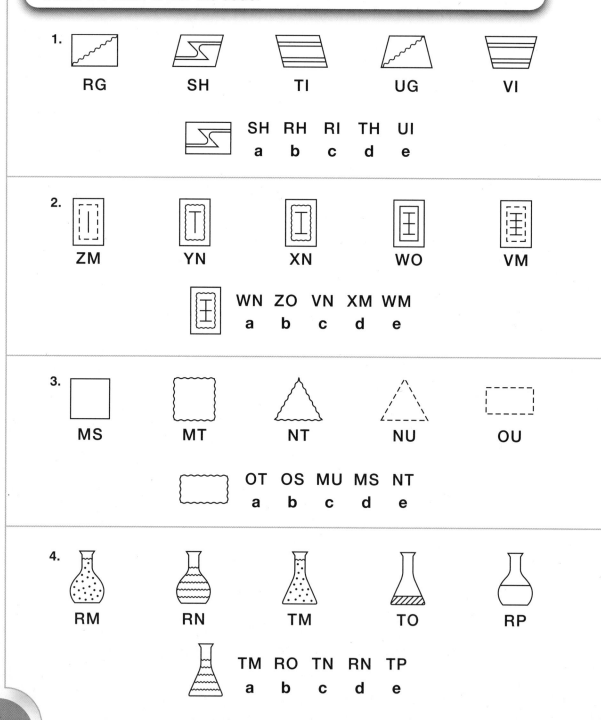

1.

RG   SH   TI   UG   VI

SH RH RI TH UI
a   b   c   d   e

2.

ZM   YN   XN   WO   VM

WN ZO VN XM WM
a   b   c   d   e

3.

MS   MT   NT   NU   OU

OT OS MU MS NT
a   b   c   d   e

4.

RM   RN   TM   TO   RP

TM RO TN RN TP
a   b   c   d   e

5.

SM   TN   SO   UM   UP

 TM UO TO SN TP
        a   b   c   d   e

/5

Example

Match the missing part of the second pair in a similar way to the first pair. Circle the letter under the missing part.

 as

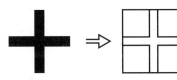

   a   b   c   (d)   e

The answer is **d.**

Now try these. Match the missing part of the second pair in a similar way to the first pair. Circle the letter under the missing part.

6. as

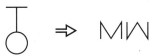

   a   b   c   d   e

7.  as

  a   **b**   **c**   **d**   **e**

8. as

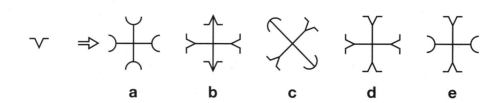

  a   **b**   **c**   **d**   **e**

9. as

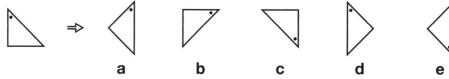

  a   **b**   **c**   **d**   **e**

10. as

  a   **b**   **c**   **d**   **e**

/5

Example

Complete the grid by finding the missing square.
Circle the letter under the square.

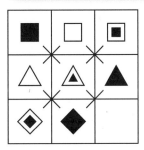

a   b   c   (d)   e

The answer is **d** because the white diamond completes the row of diamonds in the grid in a similar way to the first two rows. Also, the diagonal line in the corner of **d** makes the whole grid symmetrical.

Now try these. Complete the grid by finding the missing square.
Circle the letter under the square.

11.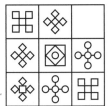

a   b   c   d   e

12.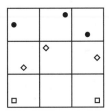

a   b   c   d   e

13.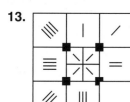

                   a   **b**   **c**   **d**   **e**

14.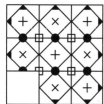

                   a   **b**   **c**   **d**   **e**

15.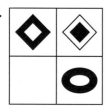

                   a   **b**   **c**   **d**   **e**

/5

Example

> Which is the odd one out? Circle the letter under it.

     a   **b**   **c**   **d**   **e**

The answer is **c** because it is the only one that has + instead of ×. In this example, the position of the shapes is not relevant.

Now try these. Which is the odd one out? Circle the letter under it.

16.

    a   b   c   d   e

17.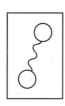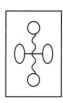

    a   b   c   d   e

18.

    a   b   c   d   e

19.

    a   b   c   d   e

20.

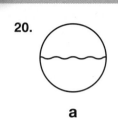 

a b c d e

/5

Example

Find the shape or pattern which completes the sequence.
Circle the letter under it.

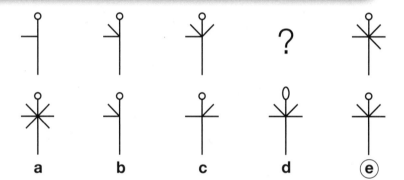

a b c d (e)

The answer is **e** because the next shape in the sequence needs four 'arms'. It is not **d** because the shape on top is not a circle.

Now try these. Find the shape or pattern which completes the sequence. Circle the letter under it.

21.

      ?

a b c d e

22.

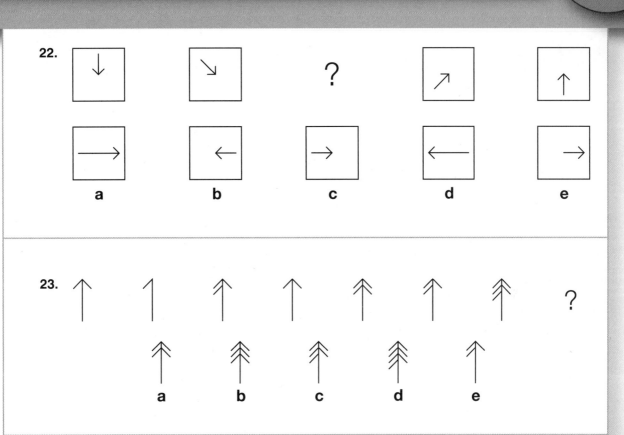

23.

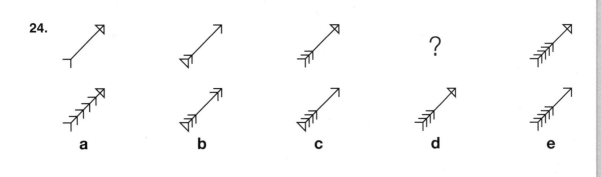

24.

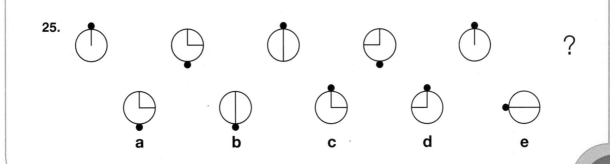

25.

26.

a

b

c

d

e

/6

/26

PAPER 6

Example

Find the shape or pattern which completes the sequence.
Circle the letter under it.

   ?

a

b

c

d

e

The answer is **e** because the next shape in the sequence needs four 'arms'. It is not **d** because the shape on top is not a circle.

Now try these. Find the shape or pattern which completes the sequence. Circle the letter under it.

1.   ?

a   b   c   d   e

2.   ?

a   b   c   d   e

3.   ?

a   b   c   d   e

4.   ?

a   b   c   d   e

5.

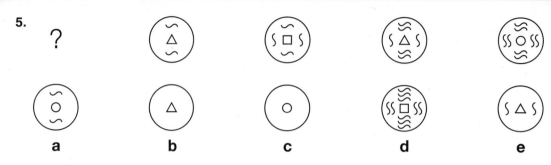

6.

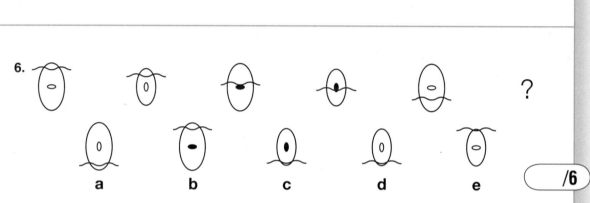

/6

Example

Which is the odd one out? Circle the letter under it.

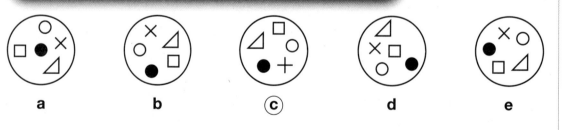

The answer is **c** because it is the only one that has + instead of ×. In this example, the position of the shapes is not relevant.

Now try these. Which is the odd one out? Circle the letter under it.

7.

a   b   c   d   e

8.

a   b   c   d   e

9.

a   b   c   d   e

10.

a   b   c   d   e

11.

a   b   c   d   e

/5

Example

Match the missing part of the second pair in a similar way to the first pair. Circle the letter under the missing part.

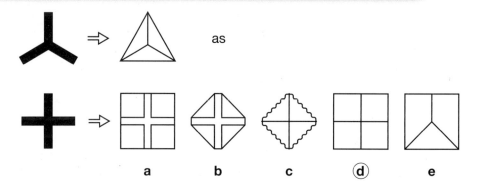

as

The answer is **d.**

Now try these. Match the missing part of the second pair in a similar way to the first pair. Circle the letter under the missing part.

12.

6 ⇒ 4   as

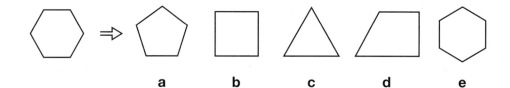

13.

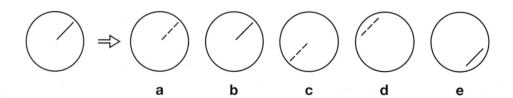

as

14.  as

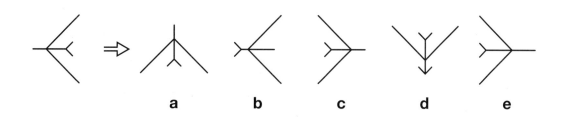

a b c d e

15.  as

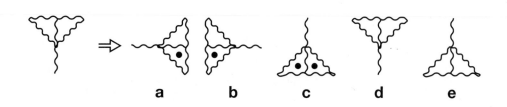

a b c d e

16. as

a b c d e

/5

Example

Complete the grid by finding the missing square.
Circle the letter under the square.

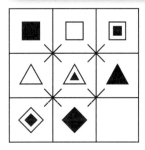

a   b   c   (d)   e

The answer is **d** because the white diamond completes the row of diamonds in the grid in a similar way to the first two rows. Also, the diagonal line in the corner of **d** makes the whole grid symmetrical.

/5

Now try these. Complete the grid by finding the missing square.
Circle the letter under the square.

17.

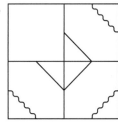

a   b   c   d   e

18.

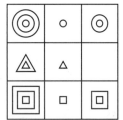

a   b   c   d   e

19.

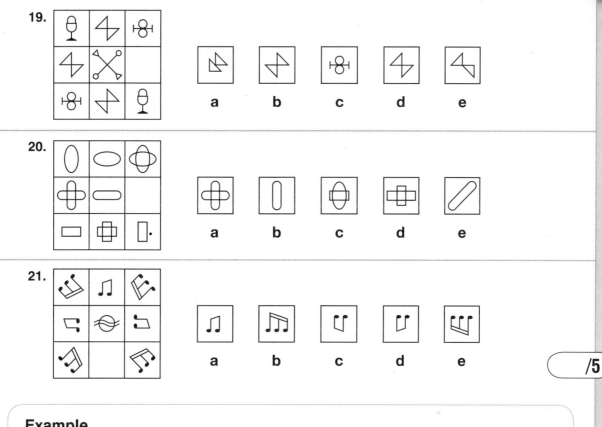

a   b   c   d   e

20.

a   b   c   d   e

21.

a   b   c   d   e

/5

Example

Look at the shapes and patterns. Work out the code for each question by putting the pattern and shape together. Circle the letter under the code.

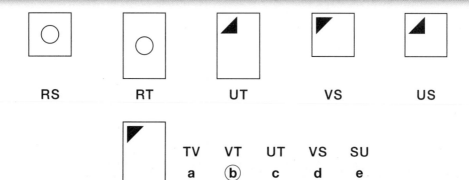

RS   RT   UT   VS   US

TV   VT   UT   VS   SU
a   (b)   c   d   e

To find the answer, you need to work out what each letter stands for. Notice that the first letter stands for the shape inside – in this case, **V**. The second letter stands for the outer shape. In this case, **T** stands for the rectangle, so the answer is **VT** and the letter **b** should be circled.

Now try these. Look at these shapes and patterns. Work out the code for the questions below by putting the pattern and shape together. Circle the letter under the code.

22.

| MR | NS | OT | PS | OR |

PT	PR	OS	NT	NR
a	b	c	d	e

23.

| GJ | HJ | GK | HL | IM |

HM	IK	HK	GM	IL
a	b	c	d	e

24.

| MZ | NZ | MY | OX | NW |

OW	NY	MX	MW	OY
a	b	c	d	e

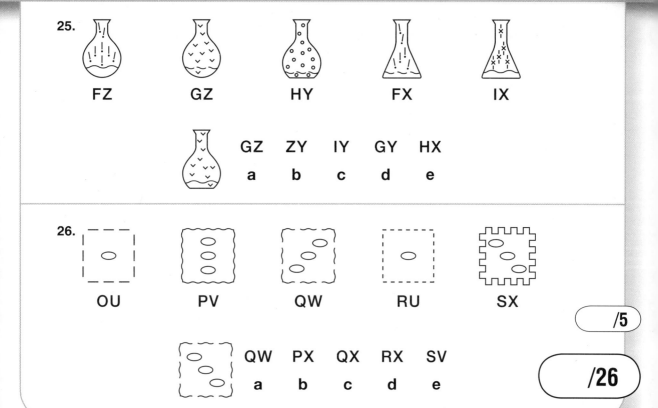

25.

FZ   GZ   HY   FX   IX

GZ ZY IY GY HX
a   b   c   d   e

26.

OU   PV   QW   RU   SX

/5

QW PX QX RX SV
a   b   c   d   e

/26

PAPER 7

Example

Which is the odd one out? Circle the letter under it.

a   b   c   d   e

The answer is **c** because it is the only one that has + instead of ×. In this example, the position of the shapes is not relevant.

Now try these. Which is the odd one out? Circle the letter under it.

1.

 a b c d e

2.

 a b c d e

3.

 a b c d e

4.

 a b c d e

5.

   a   b   c   d   e

6.

   a   b   c   d   e

/6

Example

> Find the shape or pattern which completes the sequence.
> Circle the letter under it.

         ?

   a   b   c   d   (e)

The answer is **e** because the next shape in the sequence needs four 'arms'. It is not **d** because the shape on top is not a circle.

Now try these. Find the shape or pattern which completes the sequence. Circle the letter under it.

7.

a   b   c   d   e

8.

?

a   b   c   d   e

9.

—   ?

a   b   c   d   e

10.

a   b   c   d   e

11.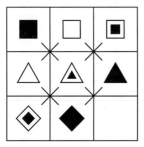

a   b   c   d   e

/5

Example

Complete the grid by finding the missing square.
Circle the letter under the square.

a   b   c   d   e

The answer is **d** because the white diamond completes the row of diamonds in the grid in a similar way to the first two rows. Also, the diagonal line in the corner of **d** makes the whole grid symmetrical.

Now try these. Complete the grid by finding the missing square. Circle the letter under the square.

12.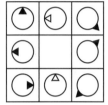

a   b   c   d   e

13.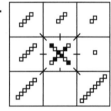

a   b   c   d   e

14.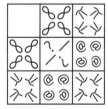

a   b   c   d   e

15.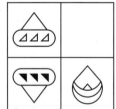

a   b   c   d   e

16.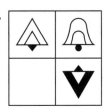

             a   b   c   d   e

/5

Example

> Look at the shapes and patterns. Work out the code for each question by putting the pattern and shape together. Circle the letter under the code.

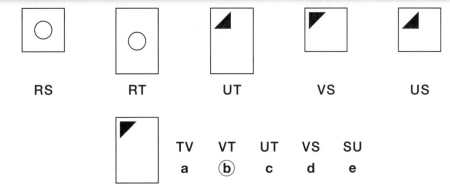

RS   RT   UT   VS   US

TV   VT   UT   VS   SU

a   (b)   c   d   e

To find the answer, you need to work out what each letter stands for. Notice that the first letter stands for the shape inside – in this case, **V**. The second letter stands for the outer shape. In this case, **T** stands for the rectangle, so the answer is **VT** and the letter **b** should be circled.

> Now try these. Look at these shapes and patterns. Work out the code for the questions below by putting the pattern and shape together. Circle the letter under the code.

17.

    FM   GN   FO   HP   IN

    GM   GP   FN   HM   HN

               a   b   c   d   e

18.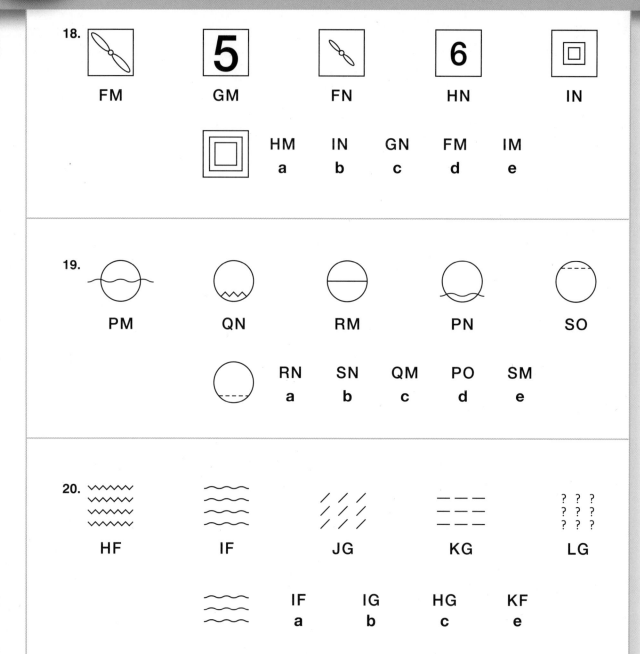

FM	GM	FN	HN	IN

HM	IN	GN	FM	IM
a	b	c	d	e

19.

PM	QN	RM	PN	SO

RN	SN	QM	PO	SM
a	b	c	d	e

20.

HF	IF	JG	KG	LG

IF	IG	HG	KF
a	b	c	e

21.

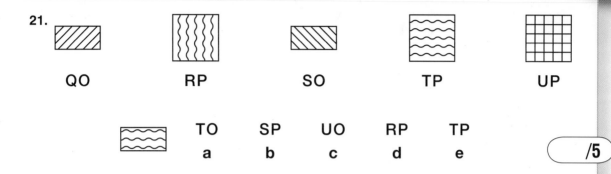

QO   RP   SO   TP   UP

TO   SP   UO   RP   TP

a   b   c   d   e

/5

Example

Match the missing part of the second pair in a similar way to the first pair.
Circle the letter under the missing part.

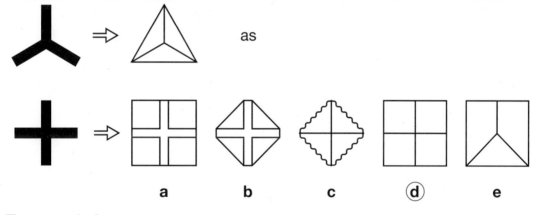

a   b   c   d   e

The answer is **d.**

Now try these. Match the missing part of the second pair in a similar way
to the first pair. Circle the letter under the missing part.

22.

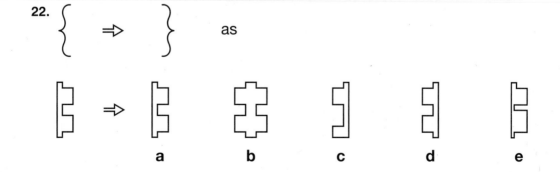

a   b   c   d   e

23.  as

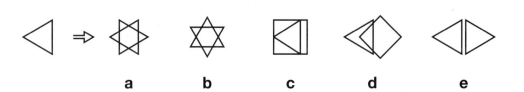

      a   **b**   **c**   **d**   **e**

24. 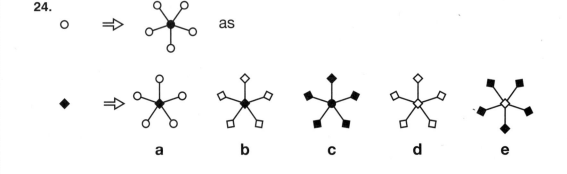 as

      a   **b**   **c**   **d**   **e**

25. 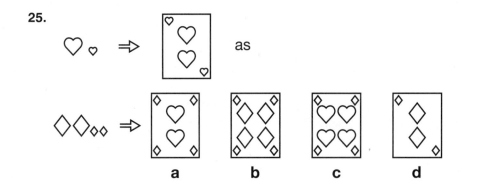 as

      a   **b**   **c**   **d**

26.

 $\Rightarrow$ as

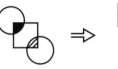 $\Rightarrow$

                            a   b   c   d   e

/5

/26

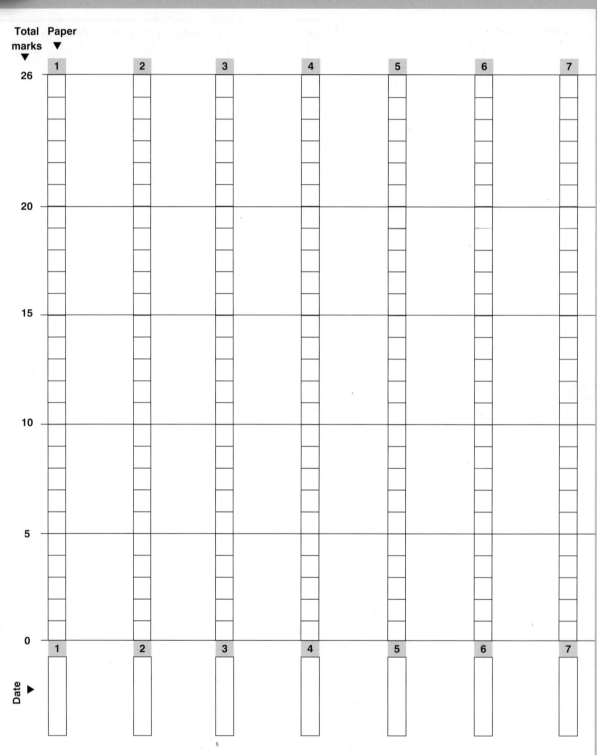

Now colour in your score!